BOUBLIL & SCHÖNBERG'S

Miss Saigon

WISE PUBLICATIONS
part of The Music Sales Group
London/New York/Paris/Sydney/Copenhagen/Berlin/Madrid/Hong Kong/Tokyo

PRESENTS

THE NEW PRODUCTION OF

BOUBLIL & SCHÖNBERG'S

JON JON BRIONES

EVA NOBLEZADA ALISTAIR BRAMMER

TAMSIN CARROLL HUGH MAYNARD KWANG-HO HONG

At certain performances **TANYA MANALANG** plays the role of Kim

Music by
CLAUDE-MICHEL SCHÖNBERG

Lyrics by
RICHARD MALTBY JNR & ALAIN BOUBLIL

Adapted from the Original French Lyrics by
ALAIN BOUBLIL

Additional Lyrics by
MICHAEL MAHLER

Orchestrations by
WILLIAM DAVID BROHN

Musical Supervision by
JOHN RIGBY & STEPHEN BROOKER

Musical Direction by
ALFONSO CASADO TRIGO

Sound Designed by
MICK POTTER

Directed by
LAURENCE CONNOR

Musical Staging by
BOB AVIAN

Additional Choreography by
GEOFFREY GARRATT

Design Concept by
ADRIAN VAUX

Projections Realised by
LUKE HALLS

Costumes Designed by
ANDREANE NEOFITOU

Lighting Designed by
BRUNO POET

Production Designed by
TOTIE DRIVER & MATT KINLEY

First performance of this production at the Prince Edward Theatre on 3 May 2014. Original London production directed by Nicholas Hytner with musical staging by Bob Avian opened at the Theatre Royal, Drury Lane, on 20 September 1989.

EMBASSY OF THE
EMBASSY OF THE UNITED
STATES OF AMERICA

Published by
WISE PUBLICATIONS
14-15 Berners Street, London W1T 3LJ, UK.

Exclusive Distributors:
MUSIC SALES LIMITED
Distribution Centre, Newmarket Road,
Bury St Edmunds, Suffolk IP33 3YB, UK.
MUSIC SALES PTY LIMITED
Units 3-4, 17 Willfox Street, Condell Park,
NSW 2200, Australia.

Order No. MF10151
ISBN: 978-1-78305-734-4

Edited by Jenni Norey
Alain Boublil photograph by Marie Zamora
Printed in the EU

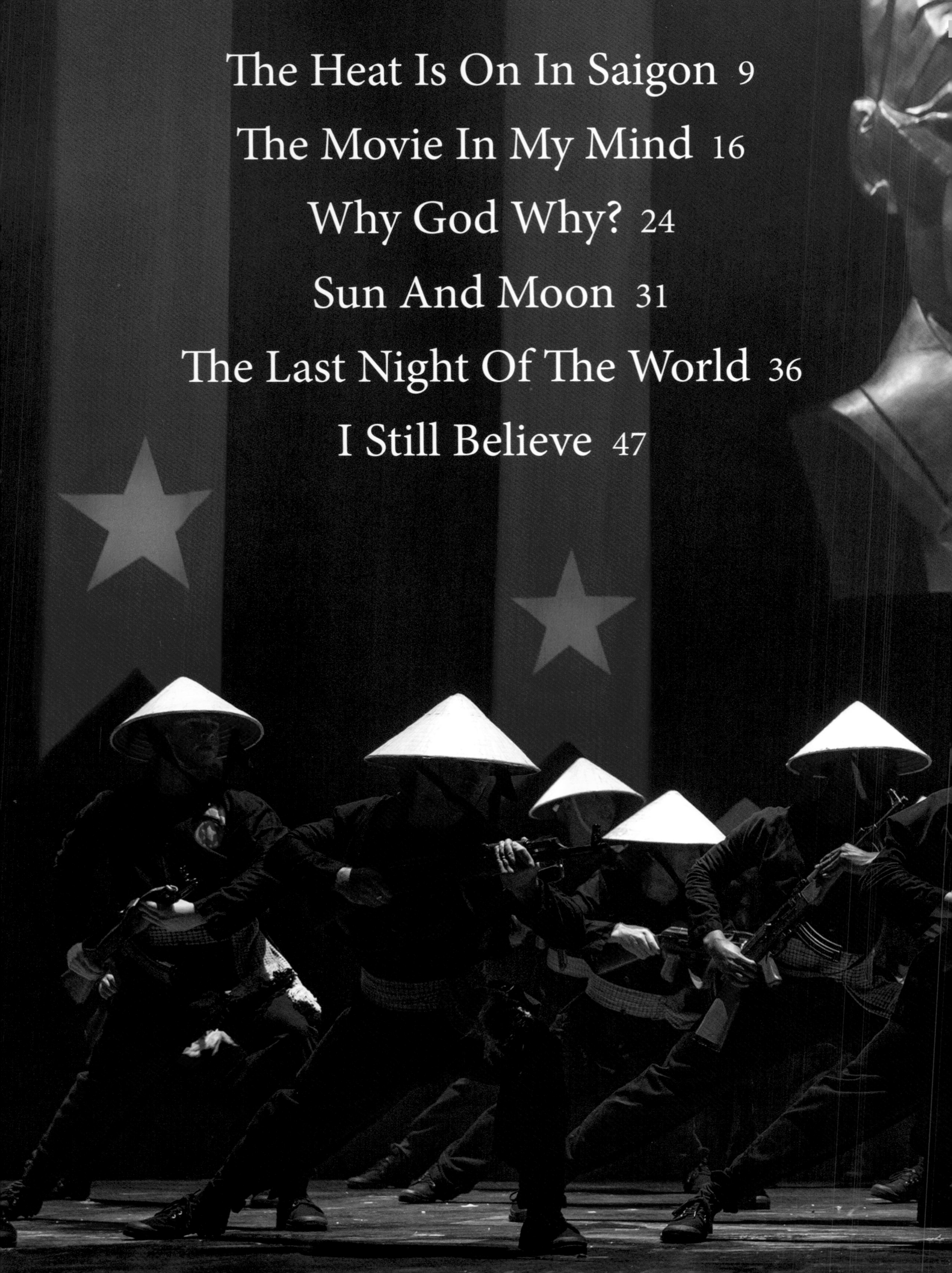

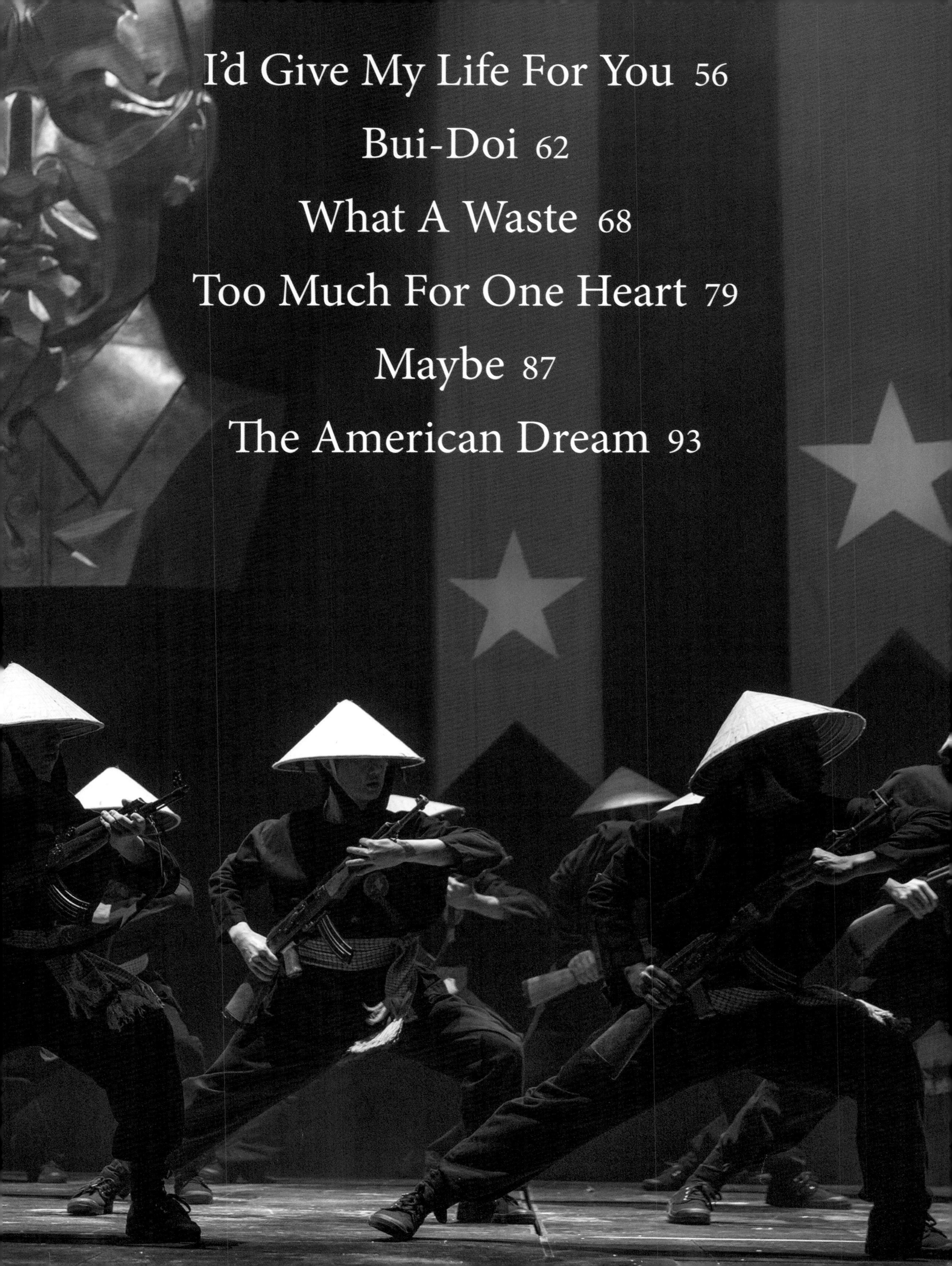

The Heat Is On In Saigon

Music by Claude-Michel Schönberg
Lyrics by Alain Boublil & Richard Maltby Jr.
Additional Lyrics by Michael Mahler

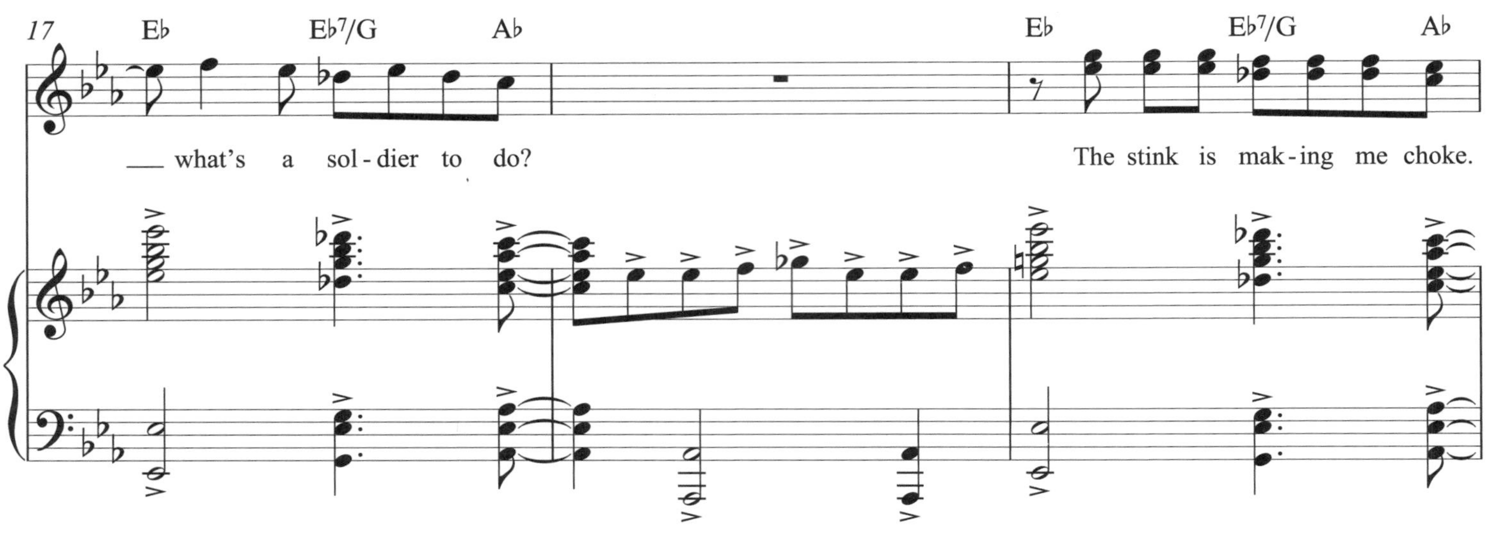
17
E♭
E♭7/G
A♭
E♭
E♭7/G
A♭
— what's a sol-dier to do?
The stink is mak-ing me choke.

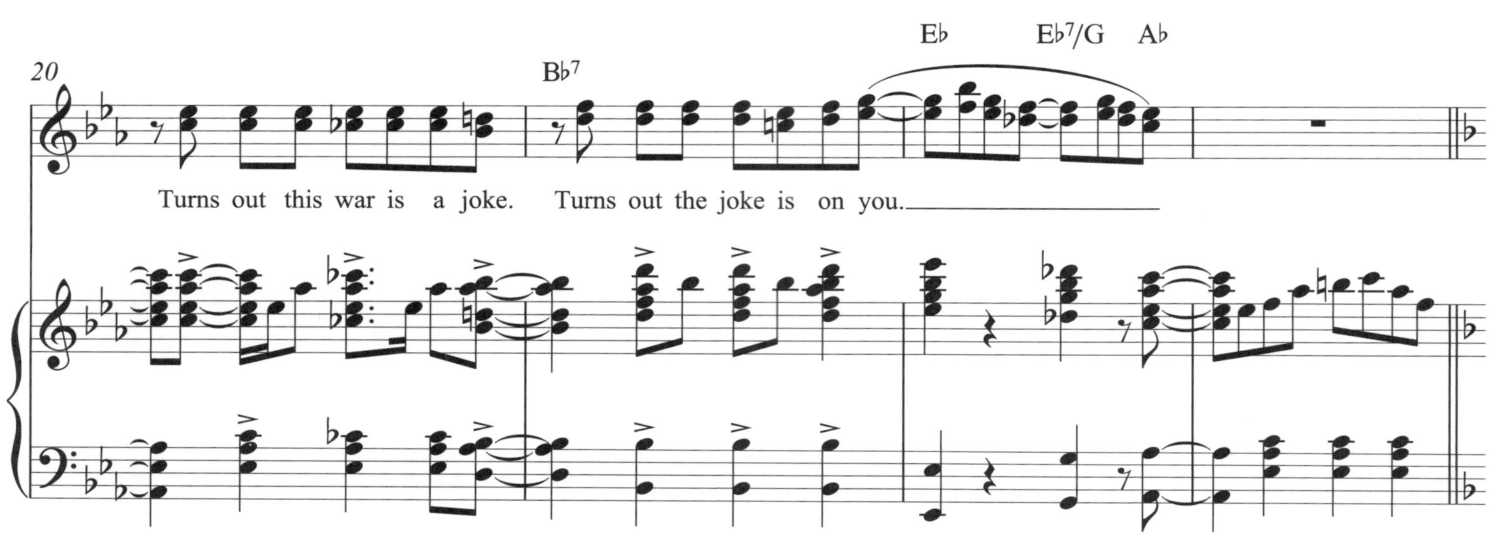
20
B♭7
E♭
E♭7/G
A♭
Turns out this war is a joke. Turns out the joke is on you.

ENGINEER:
24
F
F7/A
B♭
F
F7/A
B♭
Ah, Mon-sieur Chris, Mon-sieur John
you've come to win Miss Sai-gon.
f
mf

JOHN:
28
F F7/A B♭ B♭m C7
CHRIS:
F F7/A B♭
I got-ta get my friend laid, as a last sou-ven-ir.
I love you pal, but your bull - shit I've had up to here.
CHRIS & ENGINEER:
32
F F7/A B♭ B♭m C7
The heat is on in Sai-gon.
JOHN:
The heat is on in Sai-gon but till they tell us we're gone, I'm go-na buy you a girl.
CHRIS:
36
F F7/A B♭ B♭7
Gently
You can buy me a beer.
B
E
p

40
B
E
KIM:
B
E
I'm sev-en-teen_ and I'm new here to-day._ The

44
B
E
B
vil-lage I come_ from seems so far a-way._ All of these girls_ know much

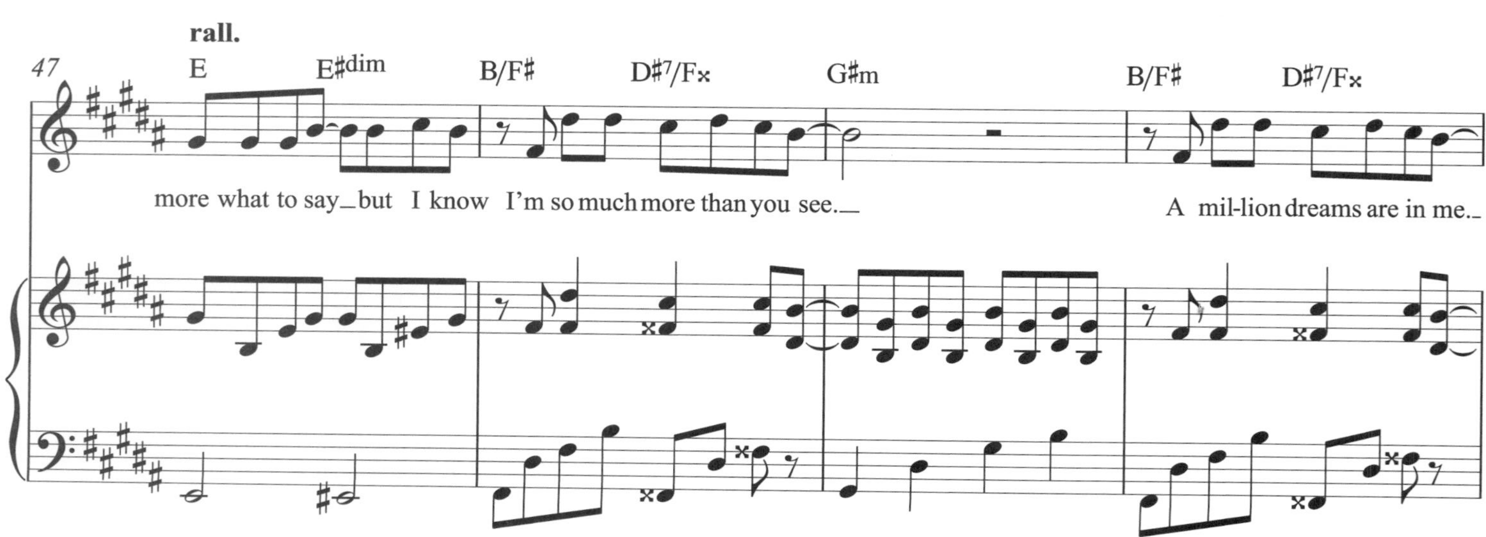
rall.
47
E
E♯dim
B/F♯
D♯7/F×
G♯m
B/F♯
D♯7/F×
more what to say_but I know I'm so much more than you see._ A mil-lion dreams are in me._

a tempo
CHRIS:
51
G♯m
Emaj7/F♯
N.C.
Je- sus, John, who is she?
sf
f

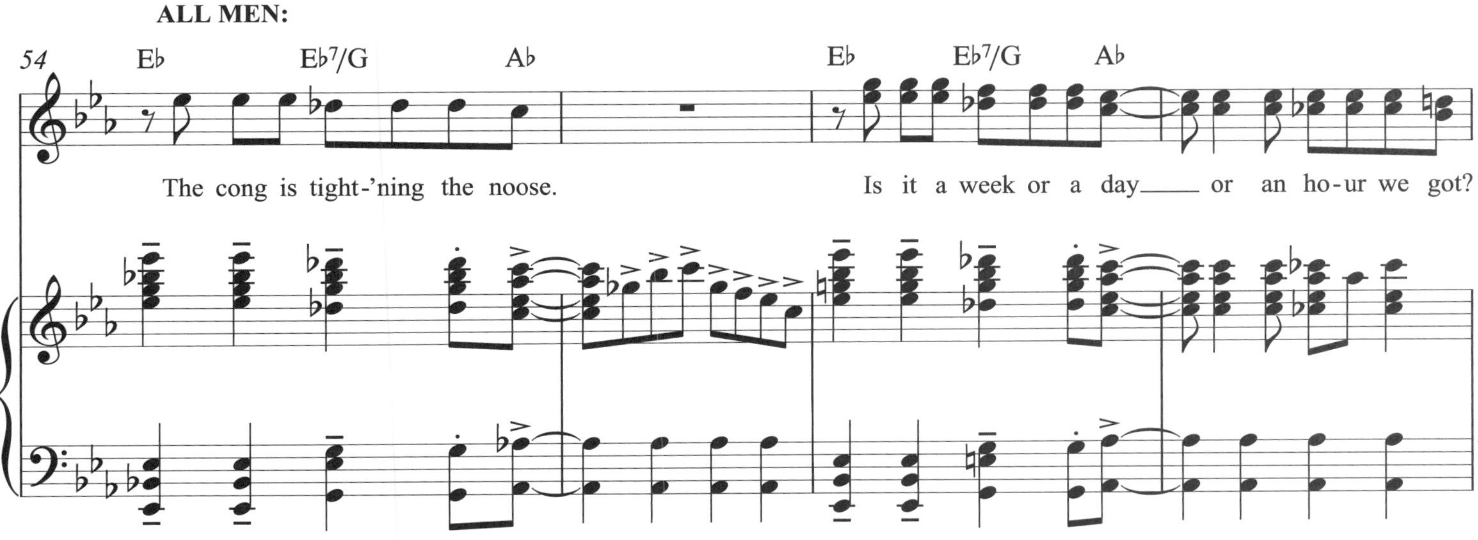
ALL MEN:
54
E♭
E♭7/G
A♭
The cong is tight-'ning the noose.
E♭
E♭7/G
A♭
Is it a week or a day or an ho-ur we got?

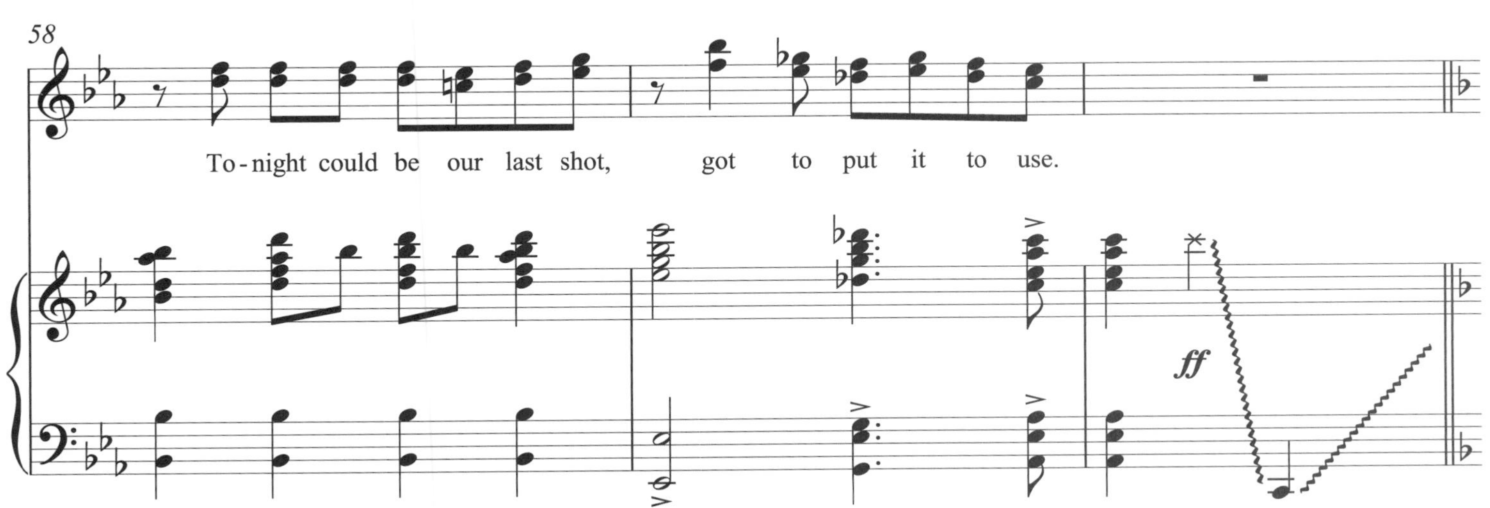
58
To-night could be our last shot, got to put it to use.
ff

ALL CHORUS:
61
F F7/A Bb F F7/A Bb
I've got a fe- ver, babe, and you're go-na catch_ it. I've got an itch, and ba-by you bet-ter scratch_ it.
f
ALL MEN:
65
F F7/A Bb Bbm C7
Mi - mi, Gi - gi, Y - vette or Y - vonne.____ Gon - na buy me a beer_
sim.
68
F F7/A Bb
ENGINEER: Yvonne... Yvette... Fifi...
C/Bb D/Bb
__ here's to you Miss Sai - gon.
mf
Mimi... Kim... Gigi... Attention s'il vous plaît. By popular demand, Miss Gigi van Tranh
72
E/Bb D/Bb A Eb/G G
f mf

is tonight's Miss Saigon!
ALL CHORUS:
77
C
C7
F
F7/A
B♭
The heat is on in Sai-gon,
ff
81
how'd we get used to the smell?
B♭m
So let's get wast-ed, get high, and get laid:
85
G
G7/B
a good-bye par-ty in hell.
90
B

The Movie In My Mind

Music by Claude-Michel Schönberg
Lyrics by Alain Boublil & Richard Maltby Jr.
Additional Lyrics by Michael Mahler

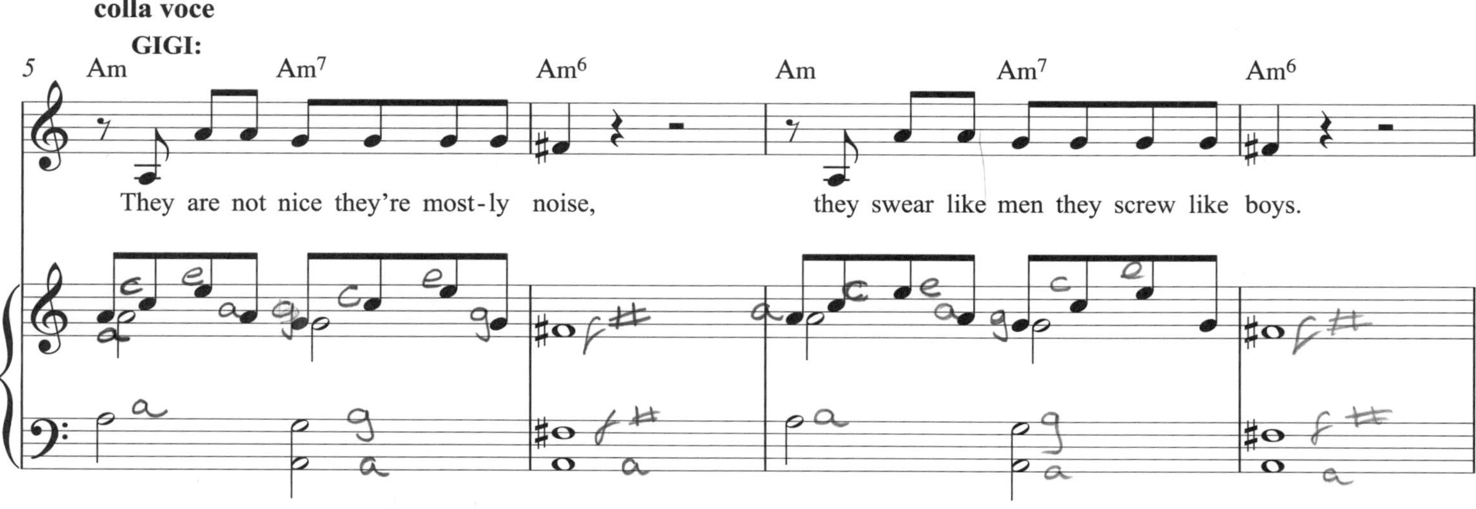

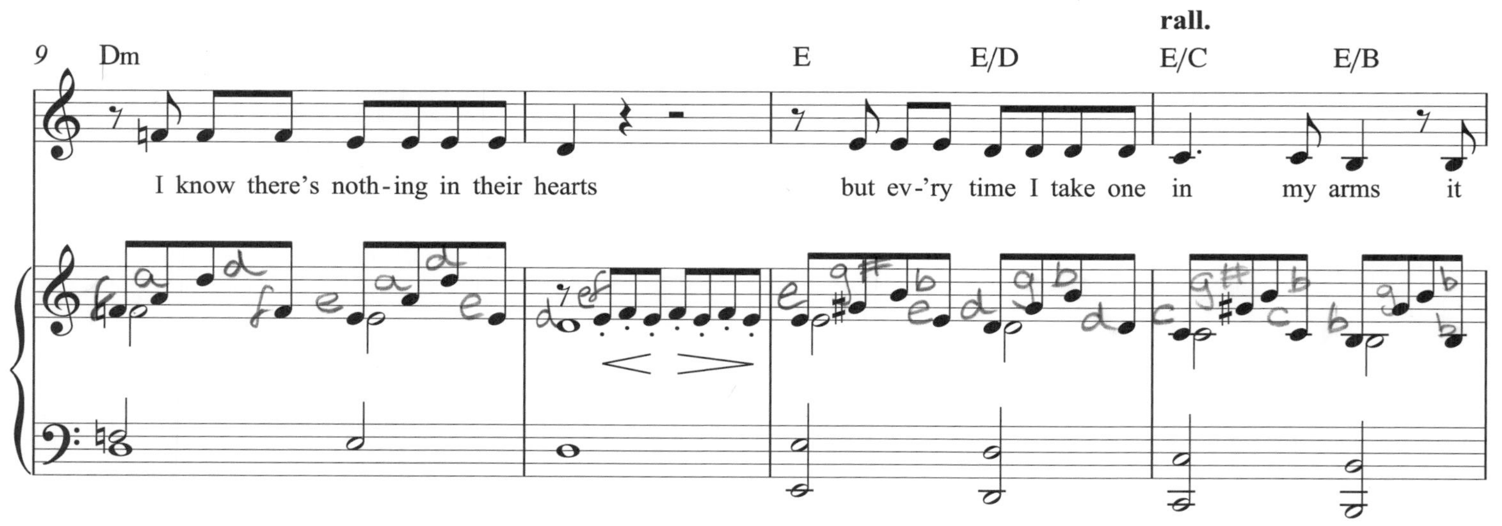

a tempo, poco più mosso
13
Am Am7 Am6 Am Am7 Am6
starts the mov-ie in my mind. The dream they leave be-
17
Dm Dm7 Dm6 Dm Dm7 Dm6
-hind, a scene I can't e-rase and in a strong G.-
21
G Cmaj7 Fmaj7 B♭maj7
-I.'s embrace flee this life,
rall.
a tempo, poco più mosso
25
E Am Am7 Am6 Am Am7
flee this place. The mov-ie plays and plays.

29 Am6 Dm Dm7 Dm6
I'll find my true ro - mance. He takes me to a
cresc. poco a poco
più mosso
32 Dm Dm7 Dm6 Em
place where I don't have to dance.
35 B7 Em A7
Our chil - dren laugh all day but all that I've been
rall.
38 Dm B7 E
through can't make my dream come true.

a tempo, appasionato
41
F
F/E
Dm7
Dream
the dream I long to
find,
ff
sfz
ff
44
F/G
rall.
C
E
the mov - ie in my
mind.
sfz
mf
pp
a tempo
KIM:
47
Am
Am7
Am6
Am
Am7
I will not cry, I will not
think,
I'll do my dance, I'll make them
pp
50
Am6
Dm
drink.
When I make love it won't be
me

rall.
a tempo
53
E
E/D
E/C
E/B
Am
Am7
and if they hurt me I'll just close my eyes and see.
GIRLS:
They are not nice they're most - ly
pp
56
Am6
Am
Am7
Am6
The mov - ie in my mind.
A dream that fills my
noise.
They kill like men, they die like boys.
59
Dm
Dm7
Dm6
Dm
Dm7
head.
A man who will not kill.
They give their cash, they keep their hearts.
But ev - 'ry night a - gain it

62
Dm6
Em
B7
Who'll fight for me in - stead.
He'll keep the fear at
starts.
mf
KIM:
65
Em
A7
Dm
bay.
So no one comes at night
68
B
rall.
E
E7/D
a tempo
F
to blow the dream a - way.
Dream
ff

71
F/E
Dm7
Dm9
rall.
F/G
F6/G
the dream I have to
find.
The mov - ie
in my
sfz
ff
sfz
più mosso
74
Cm
Cm6
Cm
mind.
f
3
Cm6
Fm
Fm6
77
3
3
80
Fm
rall.
Fm6
GIRLS:
meno mosso
B♭
And in
a strong G.
I.'s
em -
dim.
p

83
E♭maj7
A♭maj7
D♭maj7
- brace,
flee
this
life,
rall.
a tempo primo
86
G
Cm
Cm7
Cm6
KIM:
flee
this
place.
A
world
that's
far
a -
pp
89
C
C7
C6
Fm
- way,
where
life
is
not
un -
kind.
rall.
a tempo
rall.
92
F6
Cm
The
mov - ie
in
my
mind.
pp

Why God Why?

Music by Claude-Michel Schönberg
Lyrics by Alain Boublil & Richard Maltby Jr.

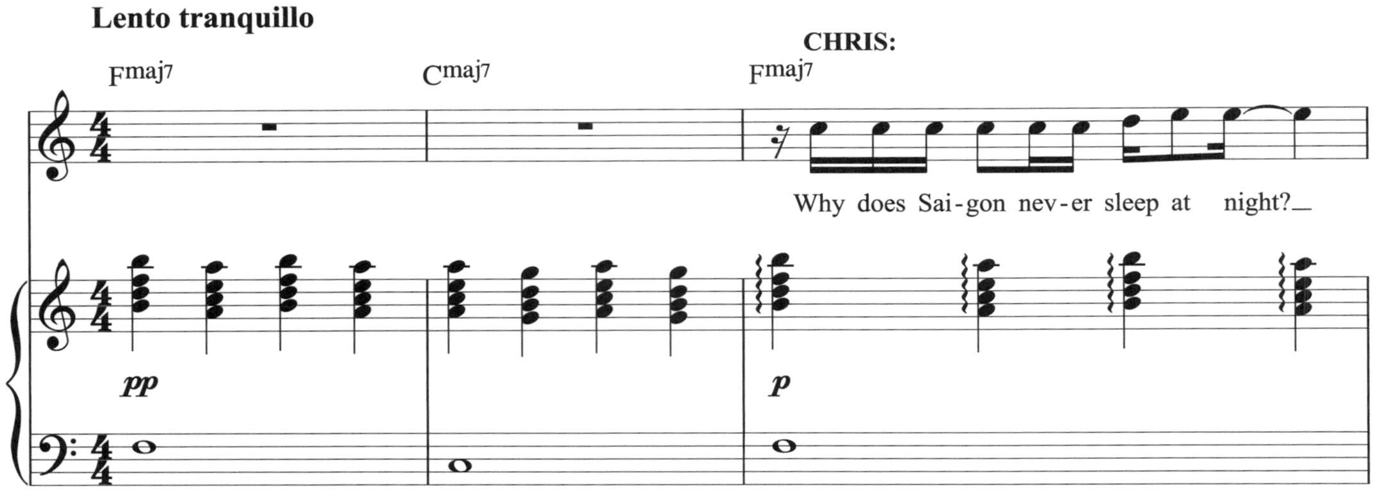

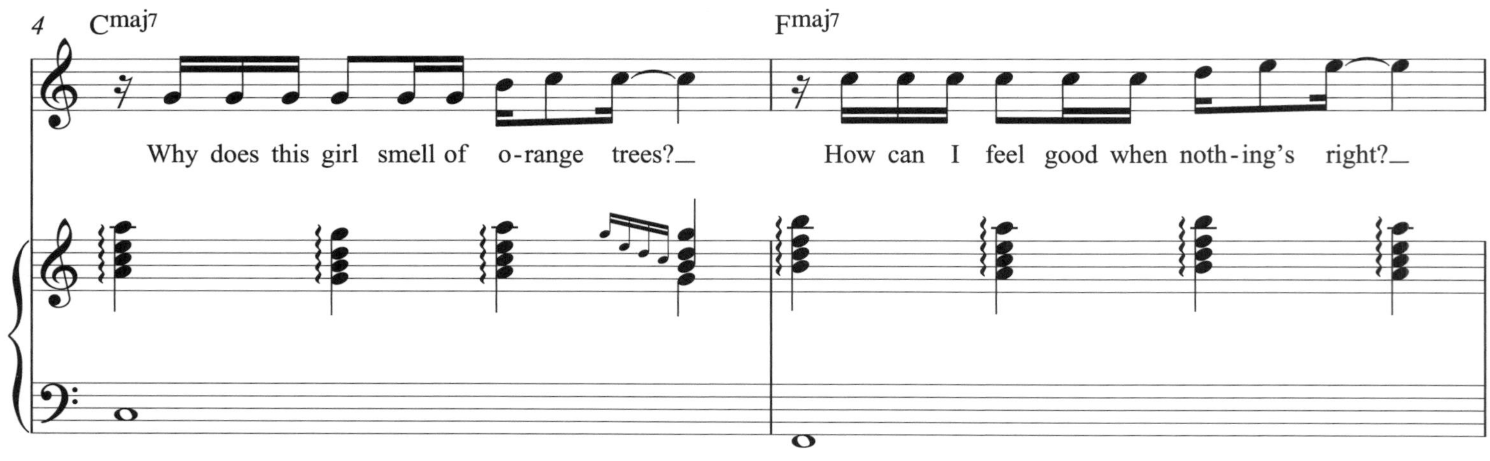

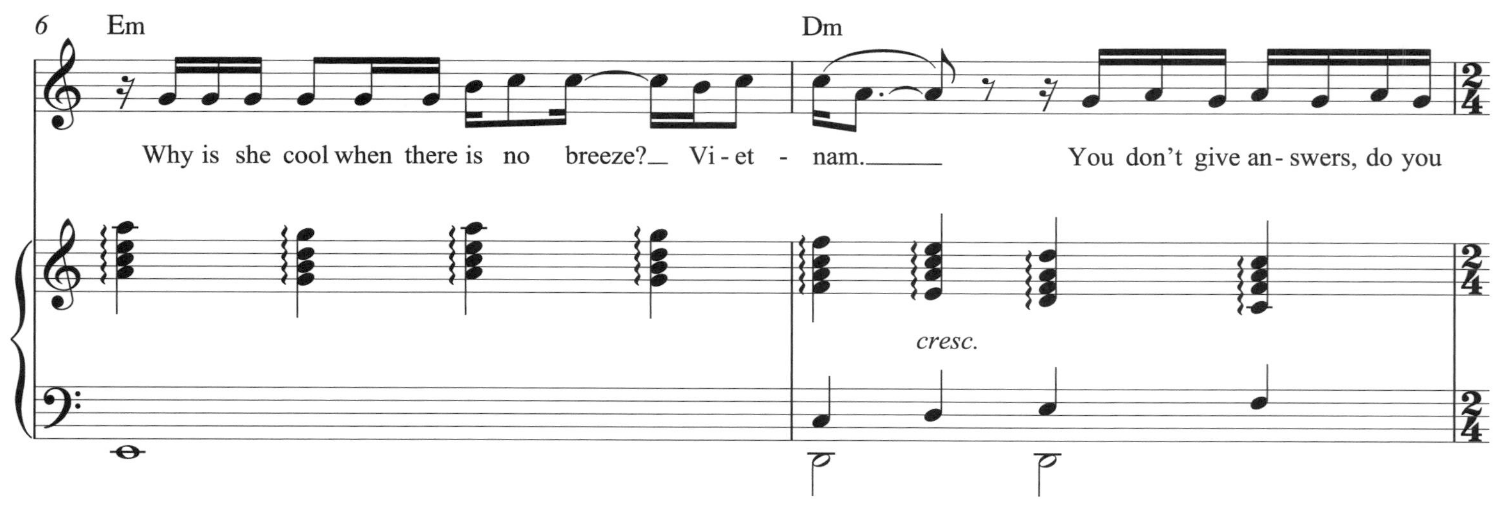

rall.
8
G
F/G
G
C
Cmaj7
friend?
Just ques-tions that don't ev-er end.
Why
God?
cresc.
mf
12 Am/C
C
Am
Am7
F/A
Am
Why to-day?
I'm all through here,
on my way.
There's
15 Dm
F/G
rall.
G
noth-ing left here that I'll miss.
Why send me now
a night like this?
a tempo
18 Fmaj7
Cmaj7
Who is the girl in this rust-y bed?
Why am I back in a fil-thy room?
p

20
Fmaj7
Em
Why is her voice ring-ing in my head?
Why am I high on her cheap per-fume? Vi-et-
22
Dm
G
-nam.
Hey look I mean you no of - fence,
but why does noth-ing here make sense?
cresc.
a tempo
25
F/G G
C
Cmaj7
Am/C
C
Am
Am7
Why God? Show your hand.
Why can't one guy
f
29
F/A
Am
Dm
F/G
un - der- stand? I've been with girls who knew much more, I've nev-er felt con-fused be - fore.

32
G
Eb
Ebmaj7
Cm/Eb
Eb
Cm
Cm7
Why me? What's your plan?
I can't help her,
f
ff
3
36
Ab/C
Cm
Ab
Cm/F
Bb(sus4)
Bb
no one can.
I want my mem-'ries as they were, but now I'll leave re-mem-b'ring her.
rall.
Faster
39
Fmaj7
Cmaj7
8va
mf
sf
ff
44
Ebmaj7
Db
p cresc.

48
G♭
A♭
G♭/A♭
A♭
G♭/A♭
A♭
52
D♭
D♭maj7
B♭m/D♭
When I went home be - fore no one talked of the war, what they knew from T. V.
sfp cresc. poco a poco
55
D♭(♯5)
Fm
didn't have a thing to do with me.
f
59
D♭
D♭maj7
B♭m/D♭
I went back and re - upped sure Sai - gon is cor - rupt, it felt bet - ter to be
sfp cresc. poco a poco

62
D♭(♯5)
B♭7
here driv - ing for the Em - bas - sy.
65
E♭m11
A♭(sus4)
'Cause here if you can pull a string, a guy like me
p cresc.
68
molto rit.
lives like a king, just as long as you don't be - lieve an - y - thing.
Lento (very gentle)
rit.
D
D/C
D/B
B♭
pp
molto cresc.

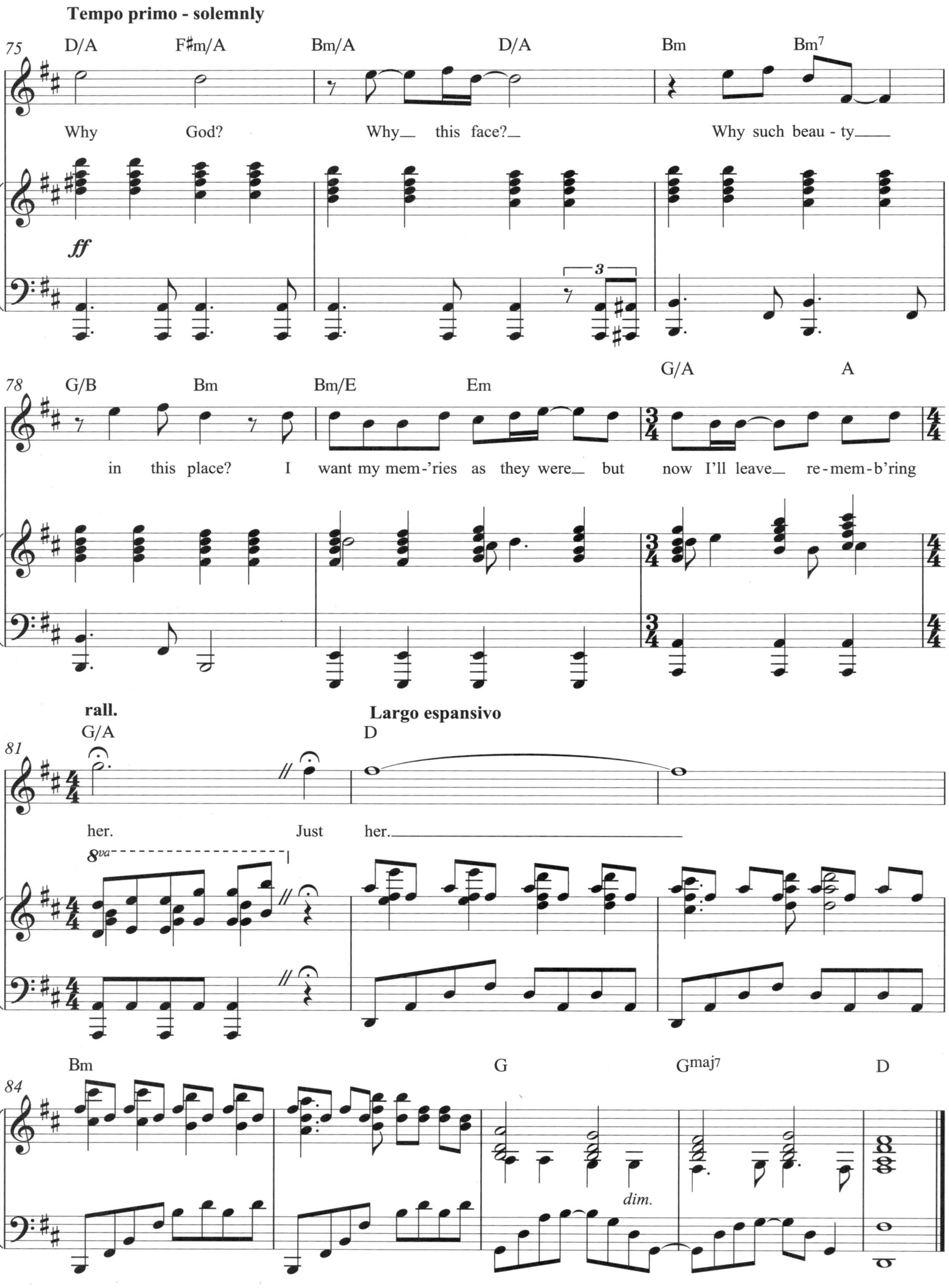

Tempo primo - solemnly

75 D/A F♯m/A Bm/A D/A Bm Bm7

Why God? Why__ this face?__ Why such beau - ty____

ff

78 G/B Bm Bm/E Em G/A A

in this place? I want my mem-'ries as they were__ but now I'll leave__ re-mem-b'ring

rall. **Largo espansivo**

81 G/A D

her. Just her.______________

8va

Sun And Moon

Music by Claude-Michel Schönberg
Lyrics by Alain Boublil & Richard Maltby Jr.
Additional Lyrics by Michael Mahler

rit.
10
G♯m
E/G♯
F♯m
B(sus4)
B7
one and the same, you and I.
poco più mosso
CHRIS:
13
E(add9)
E/A
A
You are here like a mys - t'ry,
mp dolce
16
E/G♯
E/B
B
F♯/B
B
I'm from a world that's so dif - f'rent from
19
A/B
B
C♯m
A
E/G♯
all that you are. How in the light of one

23
F♯m
B
E
night did__ we come so far.
più mosso, poco agitato
KIM:
26
B/A
A
B/A
A
B
G♯m
C♯/D
D♯
Out - side__ day starts__ to dawn.
CHRIS:
Your moon__
30
C♯/D
D♯
G♯m
A/B
B♭
E6
The birds a-wake. My
still floats__ on high. The stars shine true.
mf

rall.
G/A
A
G/A
A
F♯m
A/E
hands still shake
and we meet in the
I reach for you
and we meet in the
cresc.
più mosso
D
G/D
sky.
sky.
ff rhapsodic
G/A
A
G/A
A
F♯m/B
Bm
F♯m/A Bm/A

poco rall.
G
D/F♯
Em
A
45
mp
a tempo tranquillo
KIM:
49
D(add9)
F♯m/G
G
F♯m/G
G
You are Sun - light and I Moon joined here.
mp
53
D/F♯
Em
A
D
Bright - 'ning the sky with the flame of love.
colla voce
KIM/CHRIS:
57
G
E7
rit.
Freely
D
We are Sun - light Moon - - light.
p
pp

The Last Night Of The World

Music by Claude-Michel Schönberg
Lyrics by Alain Boublil & Richard Maltby Jr.

14
Baug
B
Baug
in a world where noth-ing can last.
I will
17
Emaj7
E/F♯
B
CHRIS:
hold you,
I will hold you.
Our lives will
20
C♯m
KIM:
C♯m/B
A
change when to-mor-row comes.
To-night our hearts drown the beat-ing drums.
mp
23
CHRIS:
D
rall.
F♯
And we'll have mu-sic all right,
tear-ing the night.
A

a tempo
26
B
B♯dim
3
C♯m7
song played on a so - lo sax - o - phone.
29
F♯7
B
KIM:
B♯dim7
A lone - ly sound. A
A cra - zy sound. A
KIM:
32
C♯m
F♯7
B
cry that tells us love goes on and on.
CHRIS:
cry that tells us love goes on and on.

35
B♯dim
C♯m7
F♯m7
Played on a so - lo sax - o - phone. It's
Played on a so - lo sax - o - phone. It's
38
B
B♯dim
C♯m7
tell - ing me to hold you tight and dance like it's the last
tell - ing me to hold you tight and dance like it's the last
41
F♯7
B
Baug
night of the world.
night of the world.

CHRIS:
44
B
Baug
On the oth - er side of the earth,
p
46
B
Baug
there's a place your life will have worth. I will
cresc.
48
Emaj7
E/F♯
KIM:
B
CHRIS:
3
take you. I'll go with you. You won't be -
tr
f
51
C♯m
C♯m/B
- lieve all the things you'll see. I know 'cause
mf

53
A
KIM:
D
If we're to - geth - er that's when we'll
you'll see them all with me.
If we're to - geth - er that's when we'll
rall.
a tempo
56
F♯
B
B♯dim
hear it a - gain. A song played on a
hear it a - gain. A song played on a
59
C♯m
F♯7
B
so - lo sax - o - phone. A cra - zy sound. A
so - lo sax - o - phone. A cra - zy sound. A

62
B♯dim
C♯m
F♯7
lone - ly sound. A cry that tells us love goes on and on.
lone - ly sound. A cry that tells us love goes on and on.
65
B
B♯dim
C♯m
3
Played on a so - lo sax - o - phone.
3
Played on a so - lo sax - o - phone.
68
F♯7
B
G♯7
It's tell - ing me to hold you tight and
It's tell - ing me to hold you tight and
3

71
C♯m
F♯
B
dance like it's the last night of the world.
dance like it's the last night of the world.
KIM:
74
G♯m
D♯m
Dreams were all I ev - er knew.
76
G♯m
D♯m
E
An - y - where
CHRIS:
Dreams you won't need when I'm through.
An - y - where

rall.
79
B/D♯
A
F♯
A
we may be
I will sing
with
you
our
we may be
I will sing
with
you
our
cresc.
a tempo
82
D
D♯dim
Em
song.
song.
8va
3
f
ff
85
A7
(8)
D
D♯dim
Em

89
A7
D
D♯dim
KIM:
Played on a
CHRIS:
Played on a
92
Em
A7
D/A
so - lo sax - o - phone.
So stay with me and
so - lo sax - o - phone.
So stay with me and
95
B7/A
Em/A
A7(sus4)
hold me tight and dance like it's the last night of the
hold me tight and dance like it's the last night of the

poco più mosso

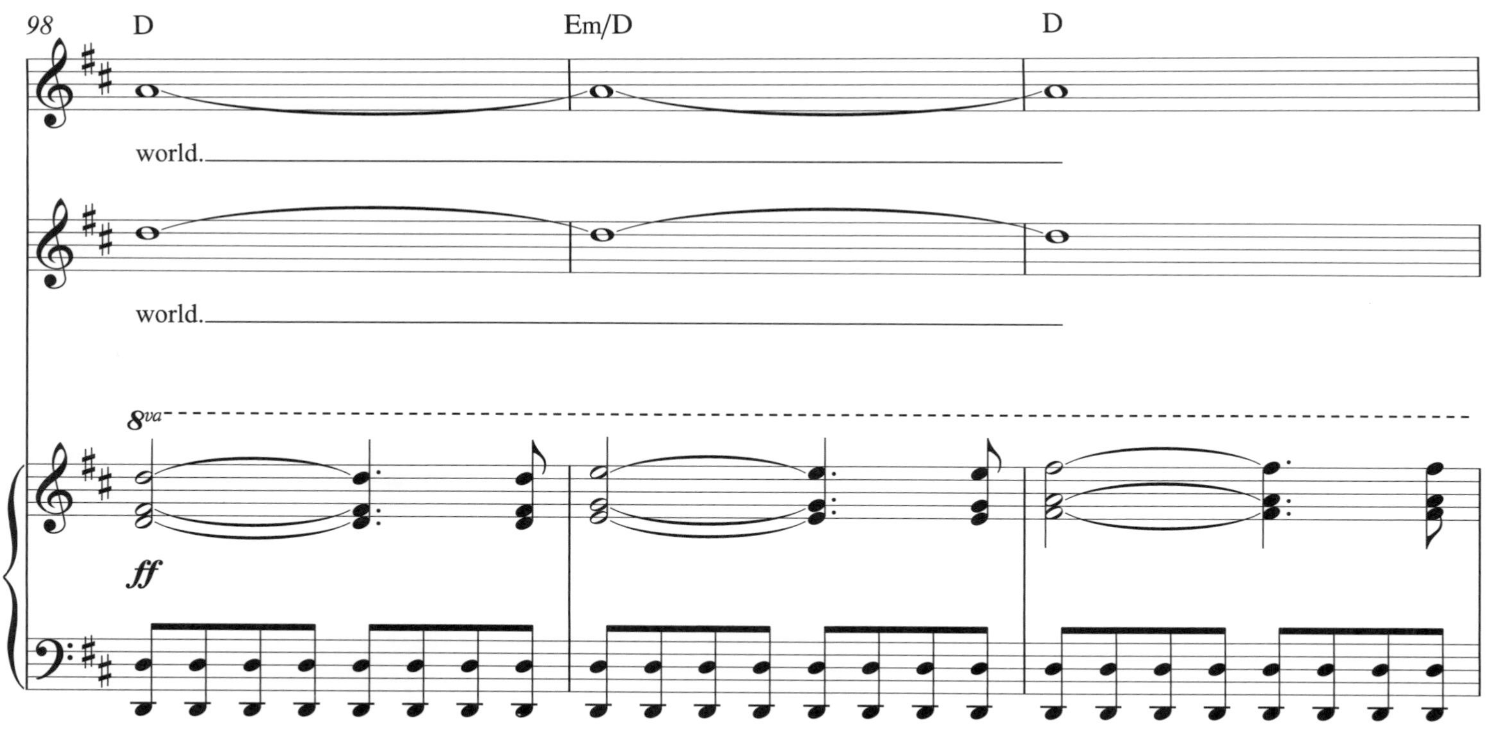

I Still Believe

Music by Claude-Michel Schönberg
Lyrics by Alain Boublil & Richard Maltby Jr.
Additional Lyrics by Michael Mahler

10
F
B♭maj7
know it was so man - y years, in the si - lence of my se - cret tears
13
A
G
rall.
A7
you are here still. I
a tempo
16
Dm
Dm/F
Gm
C7
still, I still be - lieve you
mp
20
F
F7
B♭
B♭m
will re - turn, I know you will. My heart

24
F
E♭
C7
rall.
for - ev - er - more
holds still.
Yes,
a tempo
27
Dm
Dm/F
Gm
still,
I still be - lieve
p
rall.
30
C7
F
F7
(with determination)
I know as long as I can keep be -
a tempo
33
B♭
B♭m
F
3
-liev - ing I'll live, I'll live love can-not

36
E♭
Dm
A♭
die. You will re - turn, you will re - turn and
39
G
C
A7
rall.
I a - lone know why.
a tempo
ELLEN:
42
Dm
A7/E
Dm/F
Last night I held you sleep - ing a - gain the night - mare came.
mp
45
A7/E
Dm
A/E
I heard you cry out some - thing, a

48
Dm/F
Gm7
C7
word that sound - ed like a name and it
51
F
B♭maj7
hurts me more than I can bear
know-ing part of you I'll nev - er
54
A
G
A7
rit.
share, nev - er know.
But
a tempo, poco più mosso
57
Dm
Dm/F
Gm
C7
still
I still be - lieve the

61
F7
B♭
time will come when nothing keeps us a-
64
B♭m
F
E♭
C
rall.
-part, my heart for-ev-er-more holds still.
Più mosso
68
Bdim/A♭
Bdim7
It's all o-ver, I'm here, there is noth-ing to fear.
f
70
E♭
E♭/G
Chris, what's haunt-ing you?

72
A♭m
Won't you let me in - side there is noth - ing to
A♭m/C♭
hide.
rall.
74
G♭
B(sus4)
B7
KIM:
For
ELLEN:
What's hurt - ing you?
marc.
a tempo
77
Em
Em/G
Am
still,
I still be - lieve
I will hold you all night I will make it al - right.
You are safe with

80
D7
G
I know as long as I
me. And I wish you could share what you're hid - ing in
82
G/F
C/E
can keep be - liev - ing I'll
there. What your hell must
84
Cm/E♭
G/D
F
live I'll live, you will re - turn and I know
be. You can sleep now, you can cry now,

rit.
87
Em
B♭
A
why I'm yours un - til we
I'm your wife now. For life un - til we
a tempo
90
D
Em/D
D
die.
die.
ff
Gm/B♭
rall.
D
93
8va
fp

I'd Give My Life For You

Music by Claude-Michel Schönberg
Lyrics by Alain Boublil & Richard Maltby Jr.

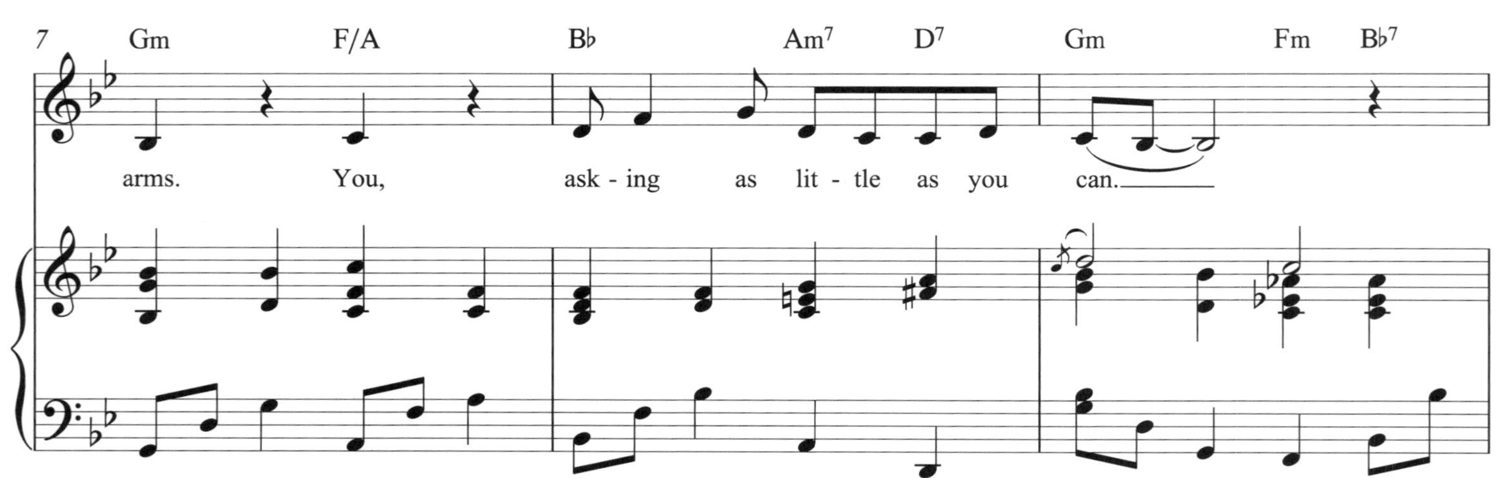

10
E♭ D7 Gm E♭ D7
Lit-tle snip of a lit-tle man,
I know I'd give my life for
rall.
a tempo
13
Gm F/A B♭ Am7 D7 Gm F/A
you.
You did-n't ask me to be born you.
16
B♭ Am7 D7 Gm Fm B♭ E♭ D/F♯
Why should you learn of war or pain.
To make sure you're not
19
Gm Gm/F E♭ D Gm
hurt a-gain,
I swear I'd give my life for you.

poco più
22
Cm G/B Cm G/B Cm G/B
I've tast-ed love be-yond all fear and you should know it's love that
mf
25
A♭ F B♭ G
brought you here. And in one per-fect night, when the stars burned like
27
Cm B♭7 E♭7
rall.
new I knew what I must do. I'll
29
A♭ Gm7 C7 F B♭ A♭/B♭
give you a mil-lion things I'll nev-er own, I'll give you a world to con-quer when you're
f
p

31
G/B
C7
rit.
a tempo
F
Em7
A7
Dm
C
grown.
You will be who you want to be, you
34
F
Em7
A
Dm
Cm7
F
B♭
C♯dim
can choose what-ev-er heav-en grants.
As long as you can have your
37
Dm
B♭
A
Dm
chance,
I swear I'll give my life for you.
f
p
40
B♭
F
B♭
F
Some nights I wake up reach-ing for him,
sub. p

42
A
Dm
C
F7
rit.
I feel his shad-ow brush my head
but there's just moon-light on my bed.
cresc.
a tempo
44
B♭m
F7/A
B♭m
F
Was he a ghost, was he a lie?
That made my bod - y laugh and cry.
f
46
Fm
E♭
D♭
C
molto rall.
Then by my side the proof I see,
his lit-tle one. Gods of the Sun bring him to
sub. p
a tempo
48
F
Em
A
D
rall.
me!
f

Maestoso
50
G F♯m7 B7 Em D/F♯ G F♯m B7
You will be who you want to be, you can choose what-ev - er heav-en
f
53
Em G7 C E♭dim Em
grants. As long as you can have your chance,
56
C B Em Em/D Cmaj7 C♯m
I swear I'd give my life for you. No one can stop what I must
8va
59
G/D D♯dim N.C. Em
do, I swear, I'd give my life for you!
(8)
sfz
ff

Bui-Doi

Music by Claude-Michel Schönberg
Lyrics by Alain Boublil & Richard Maltby Jr.

Fm
Fm/E♭
B♭/D
E♭
poco rall.
They are the fa-ces of the chil - dren, the ones we left be-hind. They're called Bui-
a tempo
A♭
B♭/A♭
A♭maj7
-doi, the dust of life con-ceived in hell and born in
D♭
B♭m7
A♭/C
D♭
strife. They are the liv - ing re - mind - er of
C7
Fm
B♭m/D♭
A♭/E♭
E♭
all the good we failed to do. We can't for-get, must not for-get that they are all our child-ren

21
A♭
E♭/G
A♭
E♭/G
too. These kids hit walls on ev-'ry side, they don't be-long in an-y place.
mp
24
Fm
Fm/E♭
D♭
E♭
A♭
Their se-cret they can't hide, it's print-ed on their face.
27
E♭/G
A♭
E♭/G
3
I nev-er thought one day I'd plead for half-breeds from a land that's torn
29
Fm
Fm/E♭
B♭/D
E♭
poco rall.
but then I saw a camp for chil - dren whose crime was be-ing born. They're called Bui-

a tempo
32
A♭
B♭m/A♭
A♭
-doi the dust of life, con-ceived in hell and born in
f
35
D♭
B♭m7
A♭/C
D♭
strife. We owe them fa - thers and a fam - 'ly a
37
C7
Fm
D♭
A♭/E♭
E♭
lov-ing home they nev-er knew be-cause we know deep in our hearts that they are all our chil-dren
40
A♭
Edim
Fm
E♭/G
A♭
too. These are souls in need, they need us to give,
sub. mp
mf

43
Am/C
E/B
Am
some-one has to pay
for their chance to live.
3
45
F
B♭
Cm/B♭
Help me try.
MEN:
They're called Bui - doi the dust of life, con-ceived in
ff
48
B♭maj7
E♭
Cm
B♭/D
E♭
And born in strife, they are the liv - ing re - min - der of
div.
hell and born in strife, they are the liv - ing re - min - der of

51
D
Gm
Em
all the good we failed to do.
all the good we failed to do.
unis.
That's why we
53
B♭/F
Gm
That's why we know
deep in our hearts
know
deep in our
hearts,
that's why we
55
B♭/F
F7
A♭9/E♭
E♭
B♭
that they are all our chil-dren too.
div.
know.
Ah.

What A Waste

Music by Claude-Michel Schönberg
Lyrics by Alain Boublil & Richard Maltby Jr.

11
Em Bm7 Em Bm7 Em Bm7
waste to pay for my keep, I'm round - ing up sheep
mf
14
Em Bm7 Em Bm7 Em Bm7
to fleece here in Bang - kok. I'm dis - graced,
f
17
G D7 G D7 G D7
I can't get a - head! There's noth - ing as dead
mf
20
G D7 G D7 G D7
as peace here in Bang - kok.
f

Am N.C.
Am
Em7
Ten cents an hour that's the most they pay.
Am
Em7
Em
Bm7
Em7
Bm7
I'll have to swim to the U. S. A.
Em
Bm7
Em
Bm7
B
D
B/G
D/F#
If you're look-ing for fun, o-ri-gi-nal sin. If you want to put out then you got-ta come

33
E
C#m
in!
HUSTLERS & VENDORS:
Girls I got girls, gor-geous girls, ver-y nice.
ff
36
C#m
(ENGINEER:)
E
Gee, is - n't Bang - kok real - ly neat?
Girls. I got girls.
39
C#m
E
The things they're sell - ing on the street. Fresh dog if that's
Girls

42
C♯
— what you'd en-joy. A girl_ or if___ you want, a boy.
worth the price.___
45
F♯m
Am
E
(HUSTLERS:)
Hey come to me.___
First drink is___ free.__
mf
48
C♯
F♯m7
B7
Don't be a lump_ you can hump___ for a small_ ex-tra fee._

ENGINEER: Humpy, humpy - batteries included.
(ENGINEER:)
51
Em
Bm7
I'm de - pressed
mf
55
for hust - ling a - mours
to Ja - pan-ese tours
sim.
58
3
is no treat in Bang - kok.
I'm the best
f
61
G
D7
but sell - ing these runts
for sex - u - al stunts
mf

64
G
D7
3
leave me beat in Bang - kok.
f
67
Am
N.C.
(ENGINEER:)
Ten cents an hour.
Screw the Si - a - mese,
70
Am
Em7
look how they're rip -
mf
Em
Bm7
73
ping off re - fu - gees.

76
B
D
B/G
D/F♯
If you're look-ing for fun, o - ri - gi - nal sin. If you want to put out then you got - ta come
(ENGINEER:)
78
E
C♯m
in. Hey, boys, don't stand a-round like wimps, watch out those guys
HUSTLERS & VENDORS:
Girls I got girls.
ff
81
E
are real - ly pimps. You want some thrills come on and grab it,
Pearls, half the price.

84
C♯
F♯m
two girls a ger - bil and a rab - bit.
Hey come to me.
mf
87
Am
E
C♯7
Look what you'll see.
ENGINEER:
90
F♯m7
B7
Hey, that's a joke mine blows smoke for a small ex - tra fee.

92
E
C♯m
TOURISTS:
You pick your kicks right off the men - u with diff - 'rent tricks
ff
95
F♯
ENGINEER:
in ev - 'ry ven - ue.
Hey, Joe, try tak - ing a lit-tle ex-cur-sion.
mf
98
D♯m
F♯
You'll all feel good from a lit-tle per-ver - sion.
Mas-sage re - quir -
TOURISTS:
Oh yeah!

101
F♯
D♯
- ing to-tal im-mer-sion, some strange po-si - tions they tell me are Per-sian.
Oh wow!
Oh no!
ENGINEER:
104
G♯m
Bm
F♯
Drinks are on me, first girl is free.
107
D♯7
G♯m/A♯
E/G♯
B/C♯
C♯m7
What can I say you get me for a small ex-tra fee.
110
E
ff

Too Much For One Heart

Music by Claude-Michel Schönberg
Lyrics by Alain Boublil & Richard Maltby Jr.
Additional Lyrics by Michael Mahler

più mosso
KIM:
7
G♯
Chris.
D♭
Yes,
tell me
p
9
A♭
ev - 'ry - thing,
I
B♭m
beg you.
How I've
11
A♭7
longed for this to
D♭
start.
All my
13
A♭/C
prayers are fin - 'ly
B♭m
ans - wered,
this is
C
too much for one

16
F
C/E
Dm
heart.
JOHN:
Kim, he went cra - zy when he lost you, spoke to
19
C
F
no one for a year. Then he
21
C7
Dm
C7
fin - 'lly said "I'm home now." My life has to go on
24
Fm
C
KIM: I don't understand.
here. Kim, let me fin - ish talk - ing
mf

rit.
Fm
E♭
A♭
please this was three whole years a - go.
a tempo
KIM:
D♭m
A♭/C
D♭m
Yes! Yes I know, I know how pain can
A♭7
Bm
G♭/B♭
3
grow when the rock you hold on - to
A
A♭
is a love miles a - way. Lis - ten

38
D♭
A♭/C
please, I al - read - y know the
mf

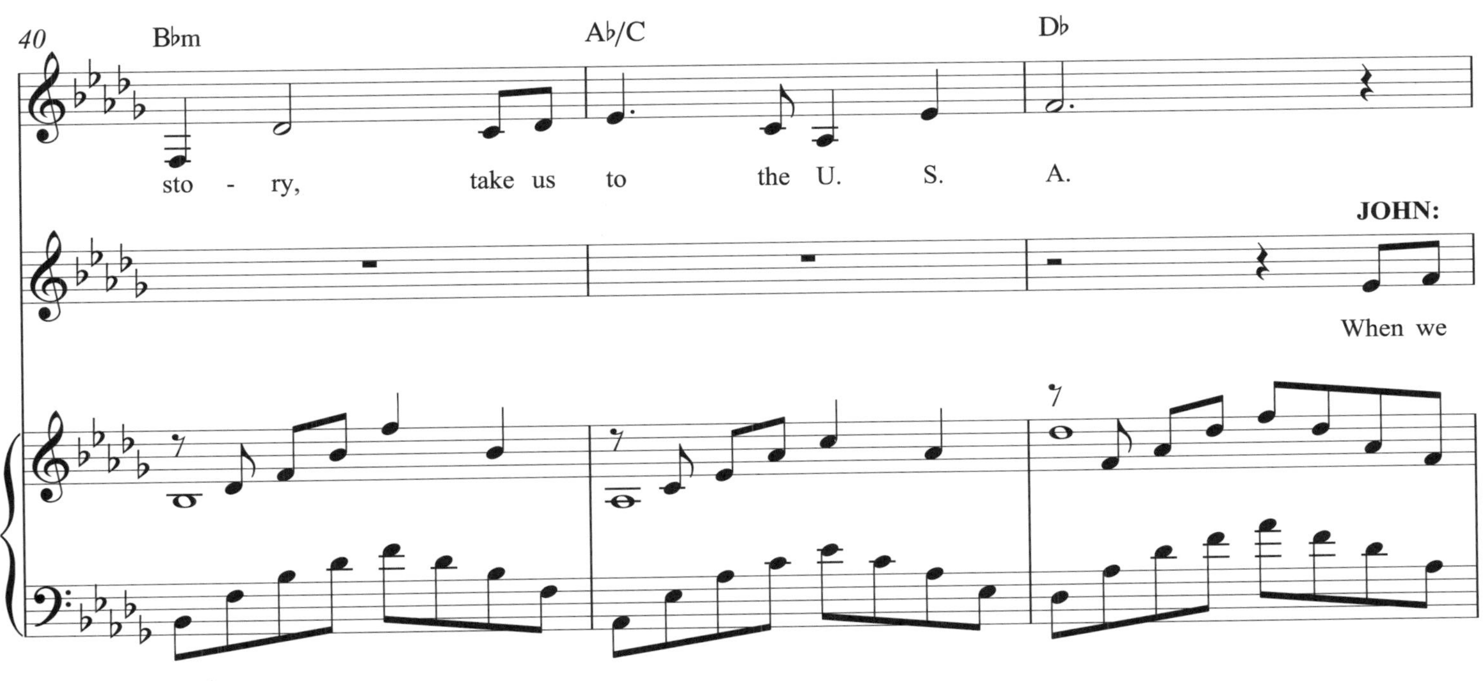
40
B♭m
A♭/C
D♭
sto - ry, take us to the U. S. A.
JOHN:
When we

43
A♭/C
B♭m
C7
fin - ish here_ you'll see him, Chris ar - rived with me to - day._

46
F
C/E
Dm
KIM:
Oh Tam! He's here,
49
C
F
C7
3
he is here, he's so near we might breathe the
52
Dm/A
C
Fm
D♭
same air to - night, your fa - ther's here. I dreamed so

(KIM:)
56
A♭
F♭
A
hard.
I kept my faith
JOHN:
I can't tell her like this.
I should not be the one
59
F
B♭
rall.
and now it's true.
Chris must first see his son.
a tempo
62
E♭
B♭/D
Now I can see we've been watched
They don't say in the files there's a wom - an in love
mf

(KIM:)
64
Cm
B♭
E♭
o - ver and our life's a - bout to start. Sun and
(JOHN:)
here, what I see in her eyes,
67
B♭7/D
Cm
molto rall.
B♭7
ten:
moon will be to - geth - er. This is too much for one
Chris still knows noth - ing of. This is too much for one
a tempo
70
E♭
B♭/D
Cm
B♭
E♭
heart.
heart.
pp

Maybe

Music by Claude-Michel Schönberg
Lyrics by Alain Boublil and Michael Mahler

colla voce
8
F♯m
Am/C
may - - be, you were nev - er mine. And yet my heart cries
a tempo
10
E
may - - be it's a trick. It's a lie. She's just try - ing to
12
C♯m
use you. But I looked in her eyes; it could kill her to
14
A
F♯m
lose you, and may - - be, just

16
Am(maj7)
E
rall.
may - - be, you need her too.
più mosso
18
C♯m
G♯
Back when we met, you were bro - ken and wild and I
p
22
F♯m
C♯m/E
held you at night, and I ached when you
25
A
cried. But des - pite what we lacked we tried

28
A♯m6
G♯
stay - ing on track. No re - gret… Yet…
Tempo I
32
E
May - - be it was fate that sud-den-ly brought her back
mf
34
C♯m
to you. And your love was true love be-fore I e-ven
36
A
knew you, if the life of your dreams is the life she is

38
F♯
rall.
giv - - - ing should I be the one to stop your dream from
a tempo
40
E
rall.
liv - - ing. If you're hers, then be hers, and for-get a-bout
cresc.
a tempo
42
F♯
me now. I've been blind for so long, but per-haps I can
f
44
D♯m
B
see now. And may - - be, just

46
G♯m
Bm
may - - be I'll find the strength I need to set you
48
F♯
free now. I'll be strong. I'll stand firm, so my tears won't be-
dim.
50
Bm
rall.
-tray me. But my heart might just break, if what may-be may
mp
52
F♯
be.
p

The American Dream

Music by Claude-Michel Schönberg
Lyrics by Alain Boublil & Richard Maltby Jr.
Additional Lyrics by Michael Mahler

11
G#7
3
C#
a tempo
we're sell - ing dreams peo - ple need.
slow
14
A
F#m6
What's that I smell in the air? The A - mer - i - can Dream.
17
A
Sweet as a new mil - lion - aire the A - mer - i - can Dream.
accel. poco a poco
20
F#m
B
Pre - packed and read - y to wear

23
B
G♯m7
my A-mer-i-can Dream.
26
B
G♯m7
Fat, like a choc-olate e-clair as I suck out the cream.
29
E
Au re-voir Miss Sai-gon,
32
B/F♯
G♯
C♯m
I'm mov-ing on.
Grab what you can till it's gone

35
F♯7
B
the A-mer - i-can Dream.
38
F♯m
G♯m
C♯7
D
Greas - y Chinks make life so slea - zy. In the States I'll have a
mf
3
41
A
F♯m
G♯m
C♯7
club that's four - starred. Men like me there have things eas - y
44
D
A
Bm/A♯
I'll have a law - yer and a bod - y - guard. To the Johns there

rall.
a tempo (pull back)
47
F♯m6/G♯
G♯(sus4)
C♯7
I'll sell blondes there that they can charge on a card.
51
A
F♯m6
What's that I smell in the air? The A-mer-i-can Dream.
mf
accel. poco a poco
54
A
Sweet as a suite in Bel-air the A-mer-i-can Dream.
57
F♯7
B
Girls can buy tits by the pair,

60
G♯m
the A-mer-i-can Dream.
63
B
Bald peo-ple think they'll grow hair,
the A-mer-i-can Dream.
65
A♭7
67
D♭
B♭m
Ass-es that stick out to there,
the A-mer-i-can Dream.

70
D♭
You can take more if you dare, the A-mer - i-can Dream.
3
73
B♭7
E♭
Banks print mon-ey from air,
76
Cm6
the A-mer - i-can Dream.
E♭
Co-caine, shot-gun and prayer,
80
C7
the A-mer - i-can Dream.
A♭
Schiltz down the drain,

84
C♭
E♭/B♭
C
pop the cham - pagne!
87
Fm
A♭/B♭
B♭7
A♭
più mosso
A♭7
It's time we all en - ter - tain the A - mer - i - can Dream.
ff
90
Cm6/G
93
G7
C
Dm
Em
F

a tempo
GIRLS:
97
B
G♯m6
Live like you have-n't a care.__ The A-mer-i-can Dream.__
BOYS:
Live like you have-n't a care.__ The A-mer-i-can Dream.__
8va
100
G♯m6
B
Take e - ven more than it's fair,__
(8)
102
G♯7
__ the A-mer-i-can Dream.__
8va

105
D♭
B♭
Call girls are lin-ing Times Square, the A-mer-i-can Dream.
Call girls are lin-ing Times Square, the A-mer-i-can Dream.
108
D♭
Bums that have mon-ey to spare, the A-mer-i-can Dream.
Bums that have mon-ey to spare, the A-mer-i-can Dream.
111
B♭
E♭
Spend when the cup-board is bare,
Spend when the cup-board is bare,

114
Cm
the A-mer - i-can Dream.
the A-mer - i-can Dream.
117
E♭
Cm
Just sell your soul, and you gain the A-mer - i-can Dream.
Just sell your soul, and you gain the A-mer - i-can Dream.
ENGINEER:
120
A♭
B
Say can you see?

GIRLS & BOYS:
123
Eb/Bb
C
Fm
Ab/Bb
Land of the free.
Soon you will buy it from me. The A-mer-i-can
127
C(#11)
Db(#11)
D(#11)
A7(b9omit3)
Dream!
Dream!
Dream!
Dream!
sfz
129
Fm
Db
mp
rall.
133
Fm
Db
ENGINEER:
137
N.C.
Fm
That's what I smell in the air my A-mer-i-can Dream.
sfz

23456789